THE Princess IN BLACK
TAKES A VACATION

THE *Princess* IN BLACK

TAKES A VACATION

Shannon Hale & Dean Hale

illustrated by
LeUyen Pham

SCHOLASTIC INC.

ISBN 978-1-338-18491-4

Text copyright © 2016 by Shannon and Dean Hale. Illustrations copyright © 2016 by LeUyen Pham. All rights reserved. Published by Scholastic Inc., 557 Broadway, New York, NY 10012, by arrangement with Candlewick Press. SCHOLASTIC and associated logos are trademarks and/or registered trademarks of Scholastic Inc.

12 11 10 9 8 7 6 5 4 3 2 1   17 18 19 20 21 22

Printed in the U.S.A.   40

This edition first printing, January 2017

This book was typeset in LTC Kennerley Pro.
The illustrations were done in watercolor and ink.

For Gus, Bronson, Linus, George, and Frankie—
superheroes all

S. H. and D. H.

To Ninja Princesses Isla and Nova

L. P.

Chapter 1

It was dawn. The Princess in Black had battled monsters all night. And so Princess Magnolia was tired.

Princess Magnolia lay down in her fluffy princess bed. She closed her eyes. She was almost asleep when . . .

Brring!

Brring!

"The monster alarm," she muttered.
"Not again."

She stumbled into the broom closet. She slipped off her frilly pajamas. She fell into her black costume. Now she was the Princess in Black.

A very sleepy Princess in Black.

She went down the secret chute.

Onto the back of her pony, Blacky.

And into the goat pasture. Just as she had fourteen other times that week.

"ROAR!" said a toothy monster.

"Did you say 'snore'?" asked the Princess in Black.

The toothy monster shook its head. "NO. ROAR."

The Princess in Black wished it had said "snore." She wished she were snoring right then.

"EAT GOATS!" said the monster.

"They're not your goats," the Princess in Black mumbled. "They're Duff's goats. Go back to Monster Land."

The toothy monster did not want to go back to Monster Land. The toothy monster was quite set on eating goats.

So the toothy monster and the
Princess in Black waged battle.

SLEEPY SLAM!

SLUGGISH SWING!

DOUBLE DOZY

DOOZY FLING!✻

The monster picked up the Princess in Black in its fist. It opened its toothy mouth. It roared again.

The Princess in Black opened her mouth. She didn't roar back. She yawned.

Just then, someone pulled the monster's tail.

Chapter 2

A boy in a mask and cape pulled the monster's tail. A boy the Princess in Black had never seen before.

"Who are you?" asked the Princess in Black. "And where is Duff the goat boy?"

"I am the Goat Avenger!" said the Goat Avenger. "And Duff the goat boy is busy. Somewhere else. Not here."

same - - - - - - ->

same

The Goat Avenger was the same height as her friend Duff. He even had the same smile. But it couldn't be Duff. Duff did not wear a mask.

same

same

"That's funny," said the Princess in Black. "Duff the goat boy is always here. This is his goat pasture. These are his goats."

"EAT GOATS!" said the monster.

The monster was still holding the Princess in Black. The monster still had a lot of teeth.

"YOU MAY NOT EAT THE GOATS!" said the Princess in Black and the Goat Avenger.

The monster winced. There were too many people with masks. It was all very confusing.

The monster put down the Princess in Black. It stuffed itself back into the hole. In Monster Land, no one wore masks.

Chapter 3

That was the fifteenth monster this week," said the Princess in Black.

She yawned again. She curled up on the grass. Blacky snuggled up beside her.

"You look tired," said the Goat Avenger.

The Princess in Black closed her
eyes. A goat licked her ear. She rolled
over. Another goat nibbled her hair.

"You need a vacation," said the Goat Avenger.

The Princess in Black opened one eye.

"What's a vacation?" she asked.

"You take a break from work," he said. "You go somewhere nice. You rest."

"That sounds amazing. But I can't take a vacation. Who will protect the goats?"

The Goat Avenger put his fist on his hip.

"Never fear," he said. "The Goat Avenger is here!"

Chapter 4

A vacation," said the Princess in Black. She led Blacky back to the castle.

"A vacation," said the Princess in Black. She crawled back up the secret chute.

"A vacation?" asked the Princess in Black. She shrugged into her frilly dress. She was no longer the Princess in Black.

"A vacation!" said Princess
Magnolia.

The Goat Avenger would stay in the pasture. He would watch out for monsters and save the goats.

Princess Magnolia packed. The best time to start a vacation was right now.

Chapter 5

Princess Magnolia rode her bicycle to the seaside. After all, her pony deserved a vacation too.

The air was salty. The sun was shiny. The sea was as blue as monster fur. It was a perfect day.

Princess Magnolia lay down in a hammock. She closed her eyes. She was just about to snore when some-one said, "Hello, Princess Magnolia."

Princess Magnolia opened her eyes. Next to her was a pile of snacks. Beside the snacks was another hammock. On that hammock was a book. Behind the book was Princess Sneezewort.

"What a surprise!" said Princess Magnolia in her cheeriest sleepy voice.

"You sound tired," said Princess Sneezewort. "You should take a nap. I'll make sure no one wakes you."

"Thank you, Princess Sneezewort," said Princess Magnolia.

"Of course," she said. "That's what friends are for."

Princess Magnolia closed her eyes again.

"Later," Princess Sneezewort whispered, "we can play checkers."

Princess Magnolia was just about to snore again when she heard a noise. "ROAR!"

Princess Magnolia kept her eyes shut. A monster? On the perfect beach? Impossible.

"*ROARRR!*"

Princess Magnolia squeezed her eyes shutter. Maybe she was already asleep. Maybe she was dreaming.

"ROAAARRRR!"

Princess Magnolia peeked with one eye.

A huge head rose out of the water. The head was on a long neck. The neck was attached to a massive body.

A sea monster was terrorizing her perfect beach.

"Sorry!" said Princess Sneeze-wort. "I didn't know how to make sure a sea monster didn't wake you."

And Princess Magnolia didn't know how to make sure a sea monster didn't hurt Princess Sneezewort.

Princess Magnolia wore glass flip-flops. Princess Magnolia sunburned easily. Second-story windows made Princess Magnolia feel woozy.

Princess Magnolia could not fight a sea monster.

Chapter 6

The Goat Avenger stood tall in the goat pasture. Fists on hips. Chin raised. Smile sparkling. He waited for monsters to come.

The goats chewed some grass.

The Goat Avenger chopped at the air. He rolled on the grass. He said, "YAAA!"

The goats swallowed. Then they chewed some more grass.

The Goat Avenger tried out some catchphrases.

BACK, MONSTERS! BACK TO YOUR INFERNAL PIT!

BEWARE!

One of the goats burped.

The Goat Avenger went over to the hole. Monster Land was down there. All week long monsters had been climbing out of that hole. The Goat Avenger had created his own monster alarm using ropes and bells. But nothing moved.

"Hello?" the Goat Avenger whispered. "Monsters?"

The goats chewed more grass.

Chapter 7

Maybe *if I just lie here the monster will go away*, thought Princess Magnolia.

"ROOOAAARRR!" said the sea monster. "EAT PEOPLE!"

The people on the beach screamed.

"People are screaming," said Princess Sneezewort.

People ran.

"People are running," said Princess Sneezewort. "Should we run too?"

People dropped ice pops in the sand.

"That boy dropped his ice pop in the sand," said Princess Sneezewort.

"EAT PEOPLE!" roared the sea monster. "PEOPLE YUM!"

Princess Magnolia sighed.

"You're right, Princess Sneezewort," she said. "We should run."

Some say that princesses don't run. But these two did. They ran very fast.

Princess Sneezewort ran toward an ice-pop stand. Princess Magnolia ran toward a bathing tent. She needed her disguise, and fast.

Nobody knew that prim and perfect Princess Magnolia was secretly the Princess in Black. But she had to keep the sea monster from eating people, especially Princess Sneezewort. After all, that's what friends are for.

Chapter 8

Duff the goat boy sat and watched the goats chew. His mask had itched. His cape had chafed. So he'd taken them off.

He wished he'd brought a book.

Clang-clang-clang.

"The monster alarm!" said Duff.

Duff shoved on his mask. He tied on his cape. He was no longer Duff the goat boy.

CLANG! CLANG!

The Goat Avenger put his fists on his hips and said, "Ha-ha!"

Nothing came out of the hole.

CLANG!
CLANG!

The rope on the monster alarm was wiggling. The goat bells were clanging. But there was no monster in sight.

Chapter 9

The Princess in Black stood on the beach. She said, "Sea monster, you may not eat people."

"ROARRR!" said the sea monster. Its tail slapped the water. A wave crashed to shore.

Maybe it can't hear me, she thought.

The Princess in Black climbed onto a rock. She cupped her hands around her mouth.

She said, "Behave, beast!"

"ROAARRRR!" said the sea monster. Its tail whipped the beach. It barely missed the ice-pop stand.

Maybe it still can't hear me, she thought.

She leaped onto its tail. She started to run up. Suddenly the tail lifted into the air.

The Princess in Black slipped. Then she slipped some more. She grabbed the tail and hugged it tight.

Don't look down, she told herself.

She looked down. She gasped. The bathing tents looked like pebbles. The people looked like ants.

A bird landed on her shoulder. "Squawk?" said the Princess in Black. That meant "Could you fly me down?"

"Squawk, squawk," said the bird. That meant "So sorry, but you're too heavy."

"Squawk . . ." said the Princess in Black. That meant "This was supposed to be a vacation. . . ."

Chapter 10

The Goat Avenger squinted into the hole. Not so much as a tentacle appeared.

Then what was setting off the monster alarm?

A mystery! The Goat Avenger straightened his mask. He tightened his cape (a little too tight). He loosened his cape. Then he followed the rope back to a tree.

A furry creature was caught in the rope. It was flailing! It was squeaking! It was . . . a squirrel.

CLANG!

CLANG!

"At last! A monster!" said the Goat Avenger.

A nearby goat bleated doubtfully.

"A squirrel could be a monster," the Goat Avenger explained to the doubtful goat. "If you're an acorn."

The Goat Avenger freed the squirrel.

He said, "Don't eat any goats."

The squirrel squeaked. It ran away. Off to find acorns to terrorize.

The goats said, "Maaaa." That probably meant that they were proud of the Goat Avenger.

But the Goat Avenger shrugged. He'd had his heart set on a real monster. A scary monster.

Chapter 11

The sea monster's tail was long, narrow, and slick. It reminded the Princess in Black of her secret chute. That gave her an idea.

SWOOP!

If she hadn't been so tired, the
sliding would have been a lot of fun.

The sea monster's back was soft and springy, like her mattress. She had to jump to get across it.

If she hadn't been so tired, the jumping would have been a lot of fun.

The sea monster's neck was high as a tower. She had to climb to get up.

Actually, even though she was tired, the climbing was a lot of fun.

She wondered about getting a sea monster for a pet. But it would never fit in her moat.

At last she reached its head. The sea monster tried to bat her off. So the Princess in Black and the sea monster waged battle.

SERPENT SLIP!

FOREHEAD CRASH!

She skimmed down to the tip of its nose. She looked it square in the eyes.

"EAT PEOPLE!" said the sea monster.

"No!" said the Princess in Black. "You may not eat people!"

The sea monster could hear her now. It frowned.

"NO?"

"No," she said.

The sea monster sniffled. Its neck drooped. Its tail sagged.

"Um . . . you could eat fish," said the Princess in Black.

The sea monster straightened up.

"YES!" it said. "EAT FISH!"

The monster dove back into the sea. The Princess in Black had no choice but to follow.

Chapter 12

The Goat Avenger swung in a hammock. He sipped lemonade. He read a comic book.

The squirrel hopped onto his shoulder. The Goat Avenger shared his lemonade. It was a good day.

Clang-clang-clang.

"Probably another squirrel," said the Goat Avenger.

He stood and turned around.

An acorn-shaped monster with one huge eye lurked beside the hole.

"AAAH!" said the Goat Avenger.

"ROAR!" said the acorn-shaped monster.

"SQUIRREL!" said the Goat Avenger. "Terrorize that acorn!"

"SQUEAK!" said the squirrel.

"AAAAHH!" said the acorn-shaped monster. It leaped back into the hole.

The Goat Avenger put his fists on his hips. He had done it! After all, he had saved the squirrel. And the squirrel had scared away the monster. Thanks to him, the goats were safe. And somewhere, thanks to him, the Princess in Black was having a vacation.

Chapter 13

The sea monster plunged into the water. The ocean rose up. A wave formed. And the Princess in Black was on top of it.

The water washed away her disguise. The wave rolled her to an island. It dumped her on the shore.

Princess Magnolia looked around. The island was tiny. Nothing for miles. No screaming people. No ear-licking goats. And no monsters.

It was perfect.

Princess Magnolia curled up in the shade of the coconut tree.

"Vacation," she said.

She closed her eyes. She said "Snore." And then she did just that.

Don Quixote

Miguel de Cervantes

Level 2

Retold by Nancy Taylor
Series Editors: Andy Hopkins and Jocelyn Potter

Pearson Education Limited

Edinburgh Gate, Harlow,
Essex CM20 2JE, England
and Associated Companies throughout the world.

Pack ISBN: 978-1-4058-8442-6
Book ISBN: 978-1-4058-6789-4
CD-ROM ISBN: 978-1-4058-6788-7

This edition first published by Pearson Education Ltd 2008

1 3 5 7 9 10 8 6 4 2

Text copyright © Pearson Education Ltd 2008
Illustrations by Santiago Caruso, map on page 59 by Witmor
The author has asserted her moral right in accordance with the
Copyright Designs and Patents Act 1988

Set in 12/15.5pt A. Garamond
Printed in China
SWTC/01

Produced for the Publishers by AC Estudio Editorial S.L.

Published by Pearson Education Ltd in association with Penguin Books Ltd,
both companies being subsidiaries of Pearson Plc

Acknowledgements

We are grateful to the following for permission to reproduce photographs:
(Key: b-bottom; c-centre; l-left; r-right; t-top)
Alamy Images: Bluemoon Stock page 60cl; Henry Westheim page 60cr; Photofusion Picture Library page
60tr; **PunchStock:** Blend Images page 58br; Glow Images page 60br; Mike Watson page 58tl

Picture Research by Alison Prior

Every effort has been made to trace the copyright holders and we apologise in advance for any
unintentional omissions. We would be pleased to insert the appropriate acknowledgement
in any subsequent edition of this publication.

For a complete list of the titles available in the Penguin Active Reading series please write to your local
Pearson Longman office or to: Penguin Readers Marketing Department, Pearson Education,
Edinburgh Gate, Harlow, Essex CM20 2JE, England.

Contents

1.1 What's the book about?

Look at the picture on the front of this book. Circle the right words.

1 The man on the right is *short / tall*.
2 The man on the left is *short / tall*.
3 The man on the right is *fat / thin*.
4 The man on the left is *fat / thin*.
5 The two men are from a *small village / big city*.
6 They are *going on a journey / arriving home*.

1.2 What happens first?

Look at the pictures. Which man's life do the sentences describe? Write A or B.

1 It is from an earlier time in the past.

2 It is a more boring life.

3 It is more dangerous.

4 People usually stay at home.

5 People enjoy fights.

6 People wear very heavy clothes.

7 This life is more possible for people today.

CHAPTER 1

Don Quixote Begins his Life of Adventure

He wanted to be one of the men in his books. He wanted to be a knight. He wanted to leave his home and have adventures.

M
r Alonso Quixada lived quietly for many years in a village in La Mancha in the middle of Spain. He was a tall, thin man, nearly fifty years old. He didn't have a lot of money, but he had friends, a nice house, an old horse, a good dog and food on his table.

But Mr Quixada also loved to read books about **knight**s. When he read these books, he was in another world. He forgot about his work and his everyday problems. The books gave him a picture in his head of a more exciting time in more interesting places.

knight /naɪt/ (n/v) *Knights* lived from about 1200 to 1500. They fought on horses and looked for adventures. When an important person *knighted* a man, that man was a *knight*.

He read all day and all night. He talked for hours and hours to his two oldest friends, Pero and Nicolás, about the stories in these books. But Mr Quixada was different from his friends. He wanted more than books and conversation. After many years he thought, 'I don't want to sit here. I want to be a knight. I'll leave this village and have **adventures**.'

Mr Quixada got ready for his new life. He found an old **suit of armour**, and he made a **helmet**. Then he thought about his dear old horse: 'A knight's horse has to have a good name. I'll call my horse Rocinante because he isn't a tired old horse now. He, too, is ready for adventures. He and I will find a new, exciting life.'

He thought for eight more days about *his* new name before an idea came to him. 'I will be Don* Quixote de la Mancha!' he said excitedly.

Every knight in the old stories also had a lovely young woman at the centre of his life. The knight told the world about her, and he fought for her. So Don Quixote had to find the right woman.

* **Don** and **Doña** are Spanish words for Mr and Mrs. Spanish speakers use these words for important people.

adventure /əd'ventʃə/ (n) When you have an *adventure*, you do something new and exciting.
suit of armour /ˌsuːt əv 'ɑːmə, ˌsjuːt/ (n) A knight wore a *suit of armour* because it was strong. People couldn't hurt him.
helmet /'helmɪt/ (n) A *helmet* is a hard hat. Knights wore *helmets* on their heads.

Aldonza Lorenzo lived in El Toboso, near his village. She was a happy, fat girl – nice, but not really clever or beautiful. But to Don Quixote she was the loveliest woman in the world. He gave her a fine new name too: Dulcinea del Toboso.

'There is music in the name,' thought Don Quixote. 'I'll fight bad men, and then I'll send them to my love. They'll tell her about my great adventures, and that will make her happy. Then they'll sing songs and write stories about the lovely Dulcinea and her knight, Don Quixote.'

Now this man of big ideas was ready for his great journey. Early one July morning, before the sun was too hot, Rocinante carried Don Quixote, in his helmet and suit of armour, away from his village and into his new life. Don Quixote wanted to make the world a better place. He smiled happily at the idea of the famous Don Quixote de la Mancha.

'But wait!' he said to Rocinante and to the sky. 'I can't fight other knights! First, somebody has to knight me!' This was a big problem for Don Quixote, but then he remembered stories from his old books. 'Somebody on the road can knight me,' he remembered. He felt happy again.

After a long day without food, drink or adventures, Don Quixote and Rocinante came to an old building. Rocinante saw a small **inn**, but in Don Quixote's eyes it was a great **castle**.

'Look at this, Rocinante!' shouted Don Quixote. 'This is a good place for knights and their horses. We'll find important people here. Let's wait. Somebody will come out and invite us inside.'

But nobody came out and Rocinante was very tired and hungry. Rocinante walked slowly to the hotel door. Two bored young country women stood there. When they saw a strange old man in a suit of armour, with a dirty face and a **lance** in his hand, they started to run into the inn.

---

inn /ɪn/ (n) An *inn* is a small hotel in the country. The *innkeeper* gives you food and drink and a room for the night.
castle /ˈkɑːsəl/ (n) A *castle* is a very big building with tall, strong walls.
lance /lɑːns/ (n) Knights carried *lances*. They fought and killed people with them.

'Don't be afraid!' Don Quixote said quickly. 'You're fine women. I want to help. Tell me your problems, and I'll fight for you!'

But they weren't fine women and people didn't usually speak to them in that way. When they laughed at him, Don Quixote started to feel angry. But the innkeeper heard the noise and came outside.

'Good day, sir,' he said in a loud, friendly way. He didn't want to laugh, but this man at his door looked very strange.

'Sir,' Don Quixote said, 'you have a fine castle here. Perhaps it is the finest in this country. Now, please take my horse. Give him good food and water because he worked hard for me today.'

The innkeeper looked at Don Quixote's old suit of armour and asked, with a small smile, 'Sir, are you a knight?'

'I am not,' Don Quixote said sadly through his helmet. 'But perhaps you can help me with that problem. Can you knight me?'

The innkeeper didn't know anything about knights, but he wanted happy customers.

'Sir, I'm the right man for the job,' he answered.

'We'll do it in the morning,' said Don Quixote excitedly. 'And tonight I'll wait with my lance and my suit of armour in the church.'

'That's an interesting plan,' the innkeeper said, 'but there isn't a church near here. You can wait out here and I'll bring you food. Have you got any money?'

'Not a penny,' said Don Quixote. 'I know everything about knights. I know that they never carry money.'

'That's a mistake, my friend,' said the innkeeper. 'Most knights go on journeys with a **squire**. The squire carries the knight's money and clean clothes. You have to get a squire. And always take money with you on your journeys.'

'Thank you. I'll remember that. And now I'll get ready for tomorrow. It's a very important day for me.'

Don Quixote put his suit of armour down in front of the inn. Then he walked up and down. Sometimes he stopped and looked at his suit of armour. Then he started to walk again. Visitors to the hotel watched out of their windows and laughed at him.

After some time, a man arrived at the inn with his **donkey**s. The animals were tired, hungry and thirsty after a long journey, so the man moved Don Quixote's suit of armour.

'Stop! Why are you moving a brother knight's armour? Don't you know that is wrong?' Don Quixote called angrily.

'What's happening here?' the man with the donkeys asked. 'Are you trying to be funny?' He kicked the armour away from the door.

'Help me, Dulcinea del Toboso!' Don Quixote shouted.

Then he ran at the man with his lance and hit him on the head very hard. The man fell to the ground and didn't move. Don Quixote put his suit of armour next to the door again and watched it carefully.

squire /skwaɪə/ (n) A *squire* was a knight's helper.
donkey /ˈdɒŋki/ (n) A *donkey* is a grey or brown animal with long ears. It is smaller than a horse.

But half an hour later, another man arrived with his donkeys. Without a word, Don Quixote ran at *that* man with his lance. He hit the man very hard on his head three or four times. Everybody in the hotel heard the noise and ran outside. They shouted and threw things at Don Quixote.

Don Quixote was very excited. 'This is the life of a knight,' he thought happily. 'I'll fight every man in this castle!'

The innkeeper ran out too, and spoke to Don Quixote.

'Listen, sir,' he said quietly. 'I looked at my books about knights. You don't have to wait for the morning. I can knight you now. Stand here, next to your armour.'

He took Don Quixote's lance, and hit him on the back with it.

'And now you're a knight, and you can leave – tonight!'

Don Quixote smiled happily, and he and Rocinante left the hotel. The innkeeper was happy too. Don Quixote didn't pay for his food, but nobody was dead.

The next day, Don Quixote was very excited because now he was really a knight. He didn't have to wait a long time for an adventure. He was near some trees and heard the cry of somebody with a problem.

'Listen, Rocinante,' said the knight very quietly. 'Somebody wants my help. I'm ready because now I'm a knight.'

Don Quixote followed the cries and found a fifteen-year-old boy without a shirt and with his arms round a tree. An angry man stood next to the tree and shouted at the boy. 'I'll teach you a lesson. You'll open your eyes and shut your mouth at work. Do you understand?' Then he hit the boy on his back.

'Stop, sir! Why are you hitting this child?' shouted Don Quixote loudly. 'You're a man, and he's a young boy. Fight with me, your brother knight, and I'll teach you a lesson about a good knight's life.'

The man saw Don Quixote's lance and felt afraid. 'Sir, the boy is a bad worker. He doesn't always watch my animals. He falls asleep on the job. I lose **sheep** every day. What can I do with him?'

'You can pay him and send him home. Or I'll put my lance in your stomach,' Don Quixote said. 'Boy, what's your name? Are you a good worker?'

'Sir, my name is Andrés. I work very hard, and he doesn't pay me,' the boy said.

sheep /ʃiːp/ (n) People eat the meat from *sheep* and make clothes from their coats.

'Pay Andrés his money, you dog, or I'll kill you!' Don Quixote shouted at the man.

'Sir, you're making a mistake,' the man tried to say. But he saw a strange and perhaps dangerous man in front of him. 'I haven't got any money with me. But I'll take Andrés to my house and pay him every penny for his work.'

'Sir,' shouted Andrés, 'I can't go with him. He'll hit me again.'

Don Quixote spoke to the man. 'Brother Knight, you have to listen to me. Do the right thing or I'll come back. Then I'll kill you. I hope that you remember this.'

'I understand,' said the man. 'I was wrong. The boy and I are going to go to my house, and I'm going to pay him.'

'Very good,' Don Quixote said happily. 'Now the world is a better place.' Then he and Rocinante turned and left.

The man and Andrés watched the knight and his horse go down the road. Then the man said, 'Andrés, I'm going to teach you a lesson.'

'But don't hurt me,' the boy said. 'Remember the knight's words.'

'I won't forget. Come here!' Then he caught the boy and hit him many more times. 'Now go and find your good, strong knight. Perhaps he'll pay you for your bad work!'

Three or four kilometres down the road, Don Quixote saw six very rich, important men on horses. They bought and sold fruit and flowers, meat and vegetables. Seven of their workers walked behind the horses.

'Here are some knights and their squires,' Don Quixote told Rocinante. 'And now I too am a knight.' He stopped in the middle of the road. No person or horse could walk past him.

'Stop!' Don Quixote shouted. 'Is Dulcinea del Toboso not the most beautiful, the most wonderful woman in the world? Tell everybody that, and you can use this road.'

The rich men smiled at the strange man in front of them.

'Sorry, old man,' one of them said with a laugh. 'We don't know this woman. How can we tell anybody about her?'

'What?!' shouted Don Quixote angrily. 'Are you saying that she is not beautiful?'

And suddenly, with his lance in his hand, Don Quixote kicked Rocinante and they ran at the men. But Rocinante fell over something in the road, and Don Quixote fell on top of him.

In his heavy suit of armour, Don Quixote couldn't move, but he shouted at the men from the ground.

'Stop, you dogs! Don't try to run away! You'll pay for this!'

The men on foot heard Don Quixote's words and one of them took his lance from him. He hit the knight many times and broke the lance. They left Don Quixote on the ground. After a long time, a man from his village found the knight. He put his friend on his donkey and took him home.

The rich men were in the next big city that night. At dinner everybody enjoyed the story of their adventure with a strange knight.

2.1 Were you right?

Look back at Activity 1.2 on page iv. Finish these paragraphs with words from the boxes.

> interesting   village   hours
> La Mancha   bored   knights   read

Mr Alonso Quixada and his friends, Pero and Nicolás, live quietly in
a village in ª .... They love to ᵇ .... about
ᶜ .... But their lives aren't very ᵈ .... They talk
for ᵉ .... , but they never leave their ᶠ ....
Pero and Nicolás are happy, but Mr Quixada is ᵍ ....

> suit of armour   past   woman   adventures
> horse   exciting   journeys   helmet

Don Quixote wants a more ʰ .... life. He's interested
in the way of life in the ⁱ .... He wants to wear a
ʲ .... and a ᵏ .... He has a
ˡ .... , Rocinante, and he has a lovely young
ᵐ .... , Dulcinea, at the centre of his life. Don Quixote
wants to go on ⁿ .... and to have º ....

2.2 What more did you learn?

Circle the right answer.

1 Aldonza Lorenzo *loves / doesn't know / hates* Don Quixote.
2 In his new life, Don Quixote wants to *make a lot of money / work in a big city / change the world.*
3 Don Quixote looks at a small inn and sees *a large castle / an old church / a train station.*
4 The innkeeper knows *no / many / three or four* knights.
5 The people at the inn think that Don Quixote is *boring / strange / kind.*
6 Don Quixote is happy because *Dulcinea writes a letter to him / he has a good dinner at the inn / the innkeeper knights him.*
7 Andrés is afraid of *Don Quixote / sheep / his boss.*

2.3 Language in use

Read the sentences in the box. Finish these sentences in the same way.

> 'I will be Don Quixote de la Mancha!' he said **excitedly**.
>
> 'I am not,' Don Quixote said **sadly** through his helmet.

1 Mr Quixada lives very .... in a small Spanish village. He is bored with his life. (quiet)

2 Don Quixote smiles .... and leaves his village for a life of adventure. (happy)

3 At the end of a long day, Rocinante is tired and walks very .... to the inn. (slow)

4 Knights have to look after their horses and their suits of armour very .... (careful)

5 Don Quixote shouts .... at Andrés's boss. (angry)

6 When Don Quixote sees the rich men, he cries, 'Stop!' very .... (loud)

2.4 What happens next?

What do you think? Are these sentences right? Talk about them and make notes.

1 Don Quixote stays at home and reads books with his friends again.

2 Don Quixote finds a squire and goes on more adventures.

3 Don Quixote wins a lot of fights.

4 Everybody likes Don Quixote because he is good and strong.

Notes

CHAPTER 2

First Adventures with Sancho Panza

'Look over there, Sancho,' said Don Quixote. 'We'll be busy now.
Thirty or more dangerous giants are waiting for us.'

D on Quixote was at home, but he was weak and very ill. He stayed in bed for a long time. Pero and Nicolás visited him often. 'Those books about knights are bad for our friend,' Pero said after one visit. 'He gets dangerous ideas from them. Let's build a big fire and throw them on it. Then he'll forget about a knight's life.'

'And let's take away the door to the room too,' Nicolás said. 'We can build a wall there. Then he can't put any more books in that room.'

After many weeks, the knight felt better. He got up and began to look round his house. 'Excuse me,' he said to his friends. 'Where are my books? I can't find them.'

'There are no books in this house,' his friends said. 'When you were away on your journey, an angry **wizard** came here. He flew inside, and after a long time he flew away again. There was smoke everywhere. Later, after the house was clean again, we couldn't find your books.'

'I read about that wizard!' Don Quixote shouted. 'His name is Frestón. I'll fight him one day for this, and I'll win!'

---

wizard /ˈwɪzəd/ (n) A *wizard* is a clever and sometimes dangerous man in stories. Strange things happen when a *wizard* is near.

When he was stronger, Don Quixote began to plan his next adventure. Pero and Nicolás weren't happy with his ideas for new adventures. They wanted a quiet life for their friend. They wanted him to stay at home.

But Don Quixote's plans were more exciting than his old life. He forgot about Pero and Nicolás and their boring lives. He began to talk to a man from his village, Sancho Panza. This fat little man had a hard life with a difficult wife, a lot of work and not very much money. He wasn't important or very clever, and he liked listening to Don Quixote. Each day the knight told him stories from his books. At night, Sancho Panza couldn't sleep. He sat at his window and thought about the exciting lives of knights and their squires.

One day Don Quixote said, 'Sancho, I'm planning to leave our village. Would you like to come with me on an exciting journey?'

'Sir, I would like that more than anything in the world. But sadly I'm not a knight.'

'My friend, you'll be my squire,' said Don Quixote. 'No job is more important than that. The two of us will do great things. Think about it! You'll be a famous man because you'll be Don Quixote's squire!'

Don Quixote got everything ready for his journey. He remembered the innkeeper's words, and this time he took money and clean clothes with him. In the middle of a dark night, he and Sancho Panza left their village without a goodbye to friends or family. They didn't want to change their plans for anybody.

The two men went down the road, Don Quixote on Rocinante and Sancho Panza on his donkey. They talked and talked.

'Will we be rich and important?' asked Sancho Panza.

'Yes, I'll fight other knights and perhaps wizards. Perhaps I'll win a fine horse for you, or a castle for your family – or possibly a small country!'

'A country? Is that possible?' asked Sancho Panza.

'Yes, this often happens with the best knights. One day I'll give you a country – a small one – and you'll be the **king**. Everybody will listen to you,' said Don Quixote.

'Really? Will my wife listen to me?' asked the squire.

'Yes,' said Don Quixote. 'Everybody!'

Sancho Panza smiled happily. 'Thank you, sir. You're very good to me.'

When the sun came up over the trees, the two adventurers saw thirty or forty **windmill**s in front of them.

'Look over there, Sancho,' said Don Quixote. 'We'll be busy now. Thirty or more dangerous **giant**s are waiting for us. I'll kill all of them and we'll be rich.'

'Giants? What giants?' asked Sancho Panza.

'There! In front of your eyes. Look! Their arms are more than three kilometres long.'

'Please look again,' Sancho Panza said kindly. He wanted to see giants, but he couldn't. 'Those aren't giants. They're windmills. Their arms are **sail**s. The wind pushes them and the sails turn.'

---

king /kɪŋ/ (n) The *king* is the most important man in a country.
windmill /ˈwɪndmɪl/ (n) *Windmills* are tall, thin buildings with sails. A *windmill* works when the wind turns the sails.
giant /ˈdʒaɪənt/ (n) *Giants* are very big, tall, strong men in stories.
sail /seɪl/ (n) When the wind pushes the *sail* on a boat, the boat moves across the water.

'I'm sorry, Sancho, but you're a beginner in adventures. Perhaps you're afraid of these giants. Wait here and I'll fight them.'

With these words, Don Quixote and Rocinante ran at the windmills. The knight shouted, 'Stop, stupid giants! Stop and fight me! I'll send you away from this place or kill you. My good Dulcinea will help me.'

When Don Quixote and Rocinante were near the windmills, the knight pushed his lance into a sail. The wind turned it suddenly. Then another heavy sail hit Don Quixote and broke his lance. He was sitting on the ground when Sancho Panza arrived next to him.

'Why didn't you listen to me, sir? They're windmills, not giants,' Sancho Panza said.

'You don't understand, friend Sancho. For a knight, things change from minute to minute. This is the work of the wizard, Frestón. He took my books from my house, and here he changed giants into windmills. He hates me and all good knights.'

'Knights have very difficult problems,' Sancho Panza said. He helped Don Quixote to stand up and climb on Rocinante again.

When the two men were on the road again, Don Quixote began to talk to Sancho Panza about his lance.

'I read about Don Diego Pérez de Vargas, a Spanish knight. He also broke his lance in a fight. The next day he found a very large tree and pulled it from the ground. He made a new lance from the wood and killed many men with it. That's my plan. I'll make a new lance from a good tree. Then you'll see some wonderful fights.'

'I'm ready, sir. Thank you for this exciting life. But did the giants hurt you badly?'

'They did, but a knight doesn't talk about his problems. I'm not dying, so I'll be quiet about it.'

'I'm very different from you,' said Sancho Panza. 'I have to talk about my problems. When my head or stomach hurts, I tell everybody about it. But I'm only a squire, and not a knight.'

'That's right, Sancho,' said Don Quixote. 'And remember one more thing. You can't help me when I'm fighting another knight. Squires can't fight knights. Don't forget this.'

'Sir, I'm not a fighter. I'll happily watch when you have a fight.'

That night, the two men stopped under a very large tree. Don Quixote found some wood for a new lance, and then it was time for bed. Sancho Panza ate and drank. Then he went to sleep. But Don Quixote knew about a knight's life from his books. He didn't eat or sleep that night. He looked at the sky and thought about his wonderful Dulcinea.

The knight and Sancho Panza had many adventures and also some accidents. Don Quixote lost his helmet and the top of one ear in a difficult fight. He hoped for adventures everywhere. When he heard a loud noise, he followed it. When he arrived at a new place, he looked round at everything carefully. He didn't always find adventures, but he and his squire were happy in this new life.

One day they were between two villages in the mountains. Don Quixote stopped and called to Sancho Panza.

'Sancho, do you see a knight over there? He's on a grey horse, and he's wearing a beautiful helmet. I read about that helmet in one of my books. Look! It shines in the sun.'

Sancho Panza opened his eyes wider and spoke slowly. 'I can see a man on a donkey with something on his head. Perhaps it's a helmet, or perhaps it's a **bowl** from his kitchen.'

'Wait here. Later today that helmet will be on my head.'

Then Don Quixote ran at the man with his lance. 'Show your lance and fight,' he shouted.

'I don't understand,' cried the man. 'I'm going to visit a man in the next village. He's dying. What do you want from me?'

'Give me your helmet.'

'It's not a helmet. It's a bowl for my work. I'm a doctor. I'm wearing the bowl on my head because it's raining.'

'That helmet is mine, you dog! Stop here and fight for it!'

The doctor didn't want to fight. He jumped to the ground and ran for his life. The bowl fell from his head, and his donkey followed slowly after him.

'It's a fine bowl,' said Sancho Panza.

bowl /bəʊl/ (n) You can eat from a plate or a *bowl*.

Don Quixote put the bowl on his head. He said, 'It's a famous helmet, but it's very big. That knight had to pay a lot of money for this helmet. Or perhaps he got it from a wizard!'

'Sir,' said Sancho Panza with a laugh, 'it's a bowl!'

'Friend Sancho, one day your eyes will open and you'll understand everything. But for now, you have to listen to me.'

'For now, sir, I'll happily listen to you. Each day I learn more about the world and about the life of a knight and his squire,' said Sancho Panza.

Day followed day and month followed month. The two men journeyed down many roads and had many interesting conversations and exciting adventures.

One day, the knight stopped and looked at something about a kilometre away from them.

'Sancho, do you see those men on horses?'

'Look again, sir,' said Sancho. 'I don't think those are horses.'

Don Quixote didn't listen to Sancho Panza. He was very excited. 'Over there is King Alifanfarón – and over there is the King of the Garamantes. He hates Alifanfarón because Alifanfarón is in love with his beautiful daughter. Look at their knights. This is going to be a good fight.' Don Quixote happily named many famous knights from his stories.

Sancho listened and didn't say a word. He couldn't see any kings or knights or horses.

'Listen, Sancho, do you hear the horses? They're excited because the knights are getting ready for the fight.'

'Don Quixote, I can only hear a lot of sheep.'

'You're afraid. Stay here. I'll come back after the fight.'

'Please, sir, stay with me,' said Sancho Panza. 'They're only sheep. They won't hurt anybody. Please come back!'

But Don Quixote heard and saw knights on horses. He and Rocinante ran into the middle of the sheep, and Don Quixote killed seven of them. People heard the noise and ran to their sheep. They shouted at the knight and threw things at him. Something hit Don Quixote on the mouth and some of his teeth fell out. He fell to the ground. The men left him there and carried away their dead sheep.

Sancho Panza ran to Don Quixote. 'Sir, they were sheep – not kings and their knights! Why didn't you listen to me?'

'Sancho, this is Frestón's work. He changes giants into windmills and knights on horses into sheep. Go down that road and you'll see them.'

After this difficult fight, Sancho Panza took Don Quixote into the mountains. 'Sir, please forget about adventures for a time,' he said. 'Sleep and eat. Get strong again.'

Pero and Nicolás found them in the mountains and took their old friend and his squire home again.

3.1 Were you right?

Look back at your notes in Activity 2.4. Then look at the pictures below. What comes first? Write 1–6 under the pictures. Then finish the sentences.

Don Quixote finds a new ....

The two men leave the village at ....

The men .... things at Don Quixote.

His friends throw Don Quixote's books onto a ....

Don Quixote runs at some ....

Don Quixote meets ....

3.2 What more did you learn?

Discuss these questions.

1 Why do Pero and Nicolás throw away Don Quixote's books?
2 How is Sancho Panza different from Don Quixote?
3 What do the knight and his squire take when they leave their village?
4 How does Don Quixote lose his lance?
5 Why doesn't Sancho Panza help Don Quixote in his fights?
6 Why does Don Quixote kill seven sheep?

3.3 Language in use

**Read the sentences in the box.
Then make sentences with these
words.**

'I **have to talk** about my problems.'

'That knight **had to pay** a lot of
money for his helmet.'

1 Don Quixote and Sancho Panza / a / tree / often / have / sleep / under / to

....

....

2 Don Quixote / a / to / lance / has / find / new

....

3 Knights / clean / and / clothes / to / don't / money / carry / have

....

....

4 Don Quixote / or / often / eat / have / sleep / to / doesn't

....

....

5 Do / fight / to / squires / knights / have

....

6 Does / have / afraid / Frestón / to / Don Quixote / be / of

....

....

3.4 What happens next?

What do you think? Match the two sentences.

1 Don Quixote loves Dulcinea.

2 Sancho Panza wants to be
   a good squire.

3 Frestón is a wizard.

4 Don Quixote likes to talk about
   knights and their adventures.

5 Don Quixote usually loses his
   fights.

a So Don Quixote thinks that his
   problems come from him.

b So he is happy when he wins one.

c So he wants to visit her.

d So he is excited when he meets
   another knight.

e So he tries to help Don Quixote.

CHAPTER 3

Old Friends or the Work of Frestón?

'This is not good,' Don Quixote said to Sancho Panza.
'This is the work of the wizard, Frestón.'

After another long stay at home, Don Quixote wanted more adventures. His first conversation with Sancho Panza on their new journey was about his love, the beautiful Dulcinea.

'Friend Sancho, our first stop will be El Toboso because I have to see my Dulcinea.'

It was after midnight when they arrived at the lovely Dulcinea's village. Everything was very quiet, and the windows were dark.

'Take me to her castle, Sancho,' said Don Quixote.

'Castle?' cried Sancho Panza. 'What castle do you mean? Aldonza Lorenzo, I mean Dulcinea del Toboso, and her family live in a little house in a dark back street. And it's the middle of the night, sir. You can't wake everybody up at this hour. You can meet your Dulcinea tomorrow.'

Outside the village, the two men found a place for the night. In the morning, Don Quixote sent Sancho Panza into El Toboso with a long letter for his beautiful Dulcinea.

'Wait here, sir,' Sancho said. 'I'll speak to Dulcinea as quickly as possible and tell her about your great fights. Then I'll come back to you.'

Half a kilometre down the road, Sancho Panza sat down under a big tree. He had to have a plan.

'What am I doing?' he thought. 'I'm looking for a beautiful young woman in a castle in El Toboso. How can I find this woman? There is no lovely Dulcinea! Don Quixote thinks that windmills are giants. He thinks that sheep are strong knights on horses. But wait! Think! I'll find a girl and take Don Quixote to her. I'll tell him that *she's* Dulcinea. He'll be happy, but she won't understand. She'll think that Don Quixote is a strange man. So she'll turn round and go home. My knight will think the

wizard is at work again. Frestón changed a beautiful woman
into a village girl. Then we can begin our
next journey.'

With this plan in his head, Sancho Panza slept under the tree for most
of the day. In the evening he woke up and saw three country girls on
donkeys on the road. He ran back and shouted to Don Quixote.

'Come quickly, sir, your lovely Dulcinea is near. She's coming to you.'

'Oh, what beautiful words! Will I speak to her now for the first time?
Is it possible?'

'Possible?' cried Sancho Panza. 'You'll see, sir! She's with two of the
women from her castle. She's wearing a beautiful dress, and she's carrying
some lovely flowers. Dulcinea and her women are sitting on three of the
finest horses in this country. Come! Come!'

'I'll have to give you something for your help, Sancho. When we win
something on our next adventure, it will be yours. Or when my three
donkeys at home in La Mancha have babies, they'll be yours.'

'Thank you for the donkeys, sir. Don't pay me with the things from
our adventures, please,' Sancho said quickly. Then he shouted, 'Look, sir,
you can see the three young women now!'

Don Quixote looked at the three country girls. 'Sancho, perhaps Dulcinea is in her castle. I can't see her anywhere.'

'Sir, where are your eyes? Can't you see her and her friends? They're coming this way at this minute.'

'I can see three country girls on donkeys,' said Don Quixote.

'Sir, you're making a big mistake. That's Dulcinea in front of you. Go and speak to your love.'

Sancho Panza ran to the three girls and stopped their donkeys. Don Quixote followed slowly behind and looked carefully at the girl on the middle donkey. She was a fat country girl in a cheap dress.

'What are you doing?' the girl shouted. 'Get out of our way. We don't have time for any stupid games.'

'This is not good,' Don Quixote said to Sancho Panza. 'This is the work of the wizard, Frestón. I know that this girl is my Dulcinea. But I can only see an ugly country girl with a loud mouth.'

'What's he talking about?' cried the girl. 'Listen to him. There's something very strange about these two.' And the three girls kicked their donkeys and left quickly.

Don Quixote followed them with sad eyes. 'Frestón really hates me. Why did he change my Dulcinea? She looked fat and ugly, and her words were loud and unkind. Where is my good, pretty girl?'

'This Frestón will always be a problem for you,' said Sancho Panza. He turned his head away from him and tried not to laugh. Sancho was never unkind to Don Quixote.

After a long, sad day, the two adventurers went to sleep under another big tree. In the middle of the night, Don Quixote heard the sound of two horses. It was very dark, but he could see a man in a suit of armour.

'Sancho!' Don Quixote said quietly. 'Here's an adventure. There's a knight and his squire near us. Look! Can you see them?'

'How's that an adventure?' asked Sancho Panza. He was tired and wanted to sleep. But he couldn't sleep because this new knight began to sing. He sang about the lovely woman at the centre of his life, Casildea de Vandalia. He sang about his fights with the knights of Navarre, of León, of Castille and of La Mancha.

'La Mancha!' Don Quixote said very quietly to Sancho. 'I'm from La Mancha, and I don't know this knight. But let's listen and learn more.'

'You'll hear more,' said Sancho Panza unhappily. 'I think he's going to sing all night.'

But the knight heard this conversation. 'Who's there?' he shouted.

Don Quixote went to the knight and sat through the dark night with him. They enjoyed a long, friendly talk.

At the same time, Sancho Panza sat under the tree and talked to the knight's squire. 'My mouth is dry with all this conversation,' said the other squire. 'I've got something in my bag for us.' He brought out a big bottle of wine and some bread and meat.

'This is a wonderful dinner,' said Sancho Panza. 'My knight is an interesting man, but I have to live on adventures. He never thinks about his stomach or about my stomach.'

'Let's enjoy our food and drink,' said the new squire. 'Those two can enjoy their ideas and their talk.' And so the two squires had a good dinner and then fell asleep.

After their long, friendly conversation, the other knight told Don Quixote about his biggest and best fight. 'I won a great fight with a famous knight. His name was Don Quixote de la Mancha.'

Don Quixote began to feel very angry. 'Sir,' he said. 'I know that you're a very good knight. Your fights are, perhaps, famous, but your fight with Don Quixote de la Mancha didn't happen. Perhaps it was with another knight.'

'No, no,' answered the strange knight, 'it really was Don Quixote. He's the tall old knight from La Mancha with very thin arms and legs, and his squire is Sancho Panza. Listen to my words or feel my lance.'

'Sir, you're wrong. Listen to me. *I'm* Don Quixote de la Mancha. Do you want a fight here and now?' And Don Quixote stood up with his lance in his hand.

'I'm not afraid of you or any knight from La Mancha. But it's late and very dark. Let's wait for the sun. We can fight in the morning.'

Sancho Panza heard the two knights and their conversation about a fight. He woke up the other squire.

'Did you hear them? First they're good friends, and now they want to fight.'

'But it's worse than that,' said the other squire. 'Now *we* have to fight too. We can't stand and watch.'

'That's not the way in La Mancha,' said Sancho Panza. 'I'll watch. I haven't got a lance, and I'm not angry with you.'

'Let's think about it in the morning,' said the other squire. 'Perhaps I can make you angry after the sun comes up.'

In the morning light, Sancho Panza could see the other squire's face. The man had the biggest nose in the world. It was as red as fire and very, very long. Sancho couldn't stop looking at it.

Don Quixote wanted to see the face of the knight next to him, but the man quickly closed his helmet. 'He's not very tall,' thought Don Quixote, 'but he looks strong. I'm not afraid, but I'd like to see his face.'

'Sir,' Don Quixote said, 'please open your helmet. I want to see the man inside the suit of armour.'

'Let's fight!' cried the knight. 'You can see my face after I win.'

'But you can see my face now,' said Don Quixote. 'Did you really fight *this* Don Quixote?'

'I did.'

'Get your horse,' shouted Don Quixote. 'I'm ready for you.'

But when Don Quixote and Rocinante began to run at the knight, Don Quixote saw the squire with the red nose. He stopped and turned to Sancho Panza. 'Do you see that nose?' he said.

'Yes, sir, can you help me to climb that tree? I'm afraid of that man and his red nose.'

Don Quixote helped Sancho Panza to climb the tree. The new knight stopped his horse and waited. But Don Quixote didn't wait for *him*. He ran at the man and hit him with his lance. The man fell to the ground. His squire ran to him and opened his helmet. Don Quixote and Sancho Panza looked at the man – and then they looked again.

'Sancho, isn't this my old friend from La Mancha, Sansón Carrasco?'

'It is,' said Sancho Panza. 'Kill him now. I think this is the work of your wizard, Frestón. Sansón never fights you, so this isn't really him.'

'You're right,' said Don Quixote. 'Let's kill him. I'm not afraid of Frestón and his games.'

'Wait, good knight!' shouted Carrasco's squire. 'He really *is* Sansón Carrasco, and I'm his squire.'

Sancho Panza looked at the squire. 'Where's your nose?' he asked.

'It's here, in my bag.'

'I know you. You're my old friend Tomé Cecial.'

'That's right, friend Sancho. We don't want to hurt anybody,' said Tomé Cecial. 'Please, Don Quixote, don't kill Don Carrasco. He read about your dangerous fights in a book by Cide Hamete Benengeli. Don Carrasco came here because he wants to help you. He wants to take you home to your friends before your adventures kill you.'

By this time, Sansón Carrasco's eyes were open. He saw Don Quixote's lance near his head. But in Don Quixote's eyes, this man was not his old friend, Sansón Carrasco. He was a knight.

'Repeat these words,' shouted Don Quixote. 'Dulcinea del Toboso is the most wonderful woman in the world, and I never won a fight with Don Quixote de la Mancha.'

'Don Quixote, you're right. My story was wrong,' said Sansón Carrasco.

'Thank you,' said Don Quixote. 'Now leave this place. Find Frestón, your teacher. I know you aren't really my friend, Sansón Carrasco.'

The two men left, but Sansón Carrasco spoke to Tomé Cecial. 'This isn't the end. Forget my old plan. I don't like to lose. I'll fight Don Quixote one day, and I'll win.'

4.1 Were you right?

Put the right names in the questions. Then answer the questions.

Sansón Carrasco   Don Quixote   Frestón   Dulcinea   Sancho Panza

Why is ....
sitting under a tree?
....
....

Is this girl's name
.... ?
....

Did ....
change Dulcinea?
....

Does Don Quixote like
talking to ....
.... ?
....

Does ....
....
win this fight?
....

4.2 What more did you learn?

Who is thinking? Write the names. Then discuss why.

One of those girls
can be Dulcinea.

I'll wear a red nose
when we find Don
Quixote.

1 ....

2 ....

Don Quixote will
pay for this!

This is Frestón's
work.

3 ....

4 ....

30

.3 Language in use

Read the sentence in the box. Then circle the correct words.

His first conversation **with** Sancho Panza on their new journey was **about** his love, the beautiful Dulcinea.

1 ᵃ *In / At / On* home, the three country girls want to tell their story ᵇ *with / at / to* everybody. 'We were ᶜ *on / from / at* the road ᵈ *about / with / to* Toboso. A short, fat man shouted ᵉ *at / with / about* us. His strange friend was ᶠ *from / behind / for* him. He was ᵍ *near / after / in* a suit of armour, and he had a helmet ʰ *into / on / of* his head. We didn't have time ⁱ *for / under / in front of* their stupid games.'

2 ᵃ *On / To / After* the fight, Sansón Carrasco speaks ᵇ *into / to / from* his squire. 'Tomé, I wanted to help Don Quixote ᶜ *before / under / inside* this fight. But he wanted to kill me. His lance was ᵈ *for / after / near* my head. I'll fight ᵉ *with / to / in* him again. He is not the strongest knight ᶠ *before / in / under* the world!'

.4 What happens next?

1 Read the name of Chapter 4. Then write *lion*, *monkey* or *sheep* under each picture.

....

2 Look at the pictures in this chapter. Match the animals with the words.

a speaks clever theatre company   ....

b milk doctor's bowl Don Quixote's hair   ....

c big teeth large box king's men   ....

31

CHAPTER 4

Exciting Adventures with Animals

'It's after the lion's dinner time. He's getting very hungry.
And lions are dangerous when they're hungry.'

Don Quixote and his squire happily began their journey again. The knight sat on Rocinante and thought about his life of adventures. When he remembered his many fights, they always ended well. He forgot about his problems and accidents, and about their many difficult journeys.

Sancho Panza felt good too. 'That was an interesting adventure, sir,' he said to Don Quixote. 'You won that fight with no problems.'

'Yes, I did,' Don Quixote said happily. 'I think that I understand Frestón's games now.'

The two friends enjoyed their conversation about wizards and old friends. Frestón made life more interesting for Don Quixote.

In a short time they met a rich man in an expensive green coat on a fine horse. The man looked carefully at Don Quixote. He was interested in stories about knights and here was a man in a suit of armour. He and Don Quixote began a long conversation about the lives of knights.

Don Quixote was happy and busy, so Sancho Panza went for a walk. He was hungry and wanted to find some food. He found a man with about twenty sheep.

'Excuse me, sir, can I buy some milk from you?'

'Yes, do you have a bottle for it?' the man asked.

'No, but I have this bowl,' answered Sancho Panza. He gave the man the doctor's bowl – Don Quixote's new helmet. The man put some milk in the bowl and took Sancho Panza's pennies.

When he got back, some men came down the road.

'Look, Squire,' Don Quixote called to him. 'Bring me my helmet. An adventure is coming this way. I have to be ready.'

Sancho Panza ran to Don Quixote with the bowl of milk. Don Quixote took the helmet from Sancho Panza.

'Wait, sir! There's something in your helmet!' shouted Sancho Panza.

'I haven't got time for games, Sancho,' Don Quixote shouted. He didn't look inside his helmet. He took it from Sancho Panza and quickly put it on his head.

'What's this, Sancho?' He had milk in his hair and on his face. 'Is something happening to my head? I'm not hot or afraid, but something is running into my eyes.'

Sancho Panza said, 'Sir, it's a strange white milk. It has to be the work of Frestón. Here, sir, give me your helmet.'

When he gave it back to Don Quixote, the helmet was clean and dry again. Now the knight was ready for his adventure.

Don Diego de Miranda, the rich man in green, looked round. He saw some men and some horses. The horses pulled a large box. But he couldn't understand Don Quixote's idea of an adventure. He asked, 'What do you see, Don Quixote?'

'Sir, there are adventures everywhere. And a wizard is following me. He's always playing games with me. I have to be very careful.'

'I think that these men are from the king's castle. Look at the colours on their coats. Perhaps there is something for the king in that large box.'

The horses were near now, and Don Quixote spoke to the driver. 'Where are you going, my friend? What have you got in that big box?'

'I've got a **lion** for the king in the box,' said the driver.

'Is it large?' asked Don Quixote.

'It's the biggest lion in this country,' said the driver. 'Now, please move. The king's waiting for us. And it's after the lion's dinner time. He's getting very hungry. And lions are dangerous when they're hungry.'

'I'm not afraid of a lion. This is one of Frestón's games. Jump down, driver, and open the box. I want to see this dangerous animal.'

Sancho Panza ran to Don Diego de Miranda. 'Sir,' he said, 'please stop him. The lion will kill all of us.'

'Does he really want to fight a lion? What's wrong with him?' asked Don Diego.

'Nothing, really,' said Sancho Panza, 'but he's always looking for a good adventure. He's a knight, you know.'

Don Diego spoke to Don Quixote. 'Sir, think about this. This is the king's lion. Knights don't fight the king or his animals.'

'Sir, this is my adventure. The wizard Frestón put this lion here for me. Stay with my squire and watch.' He turned to the driver. 'Now, open that box or you'll die.'

'Please, sir, give me a minute. I'll move the king's men and his horses.'

'Move them quickly!' shouted Don Quixote.

'You know that I don't want to open this box,' the driver cried to the king's men. 'I'm only doing it because I have to.'

---

lion /ˈlaɪən/ (n) *Lions* are big cats from Africa and India.

34

Sancho Panza ran to Don Quixote. 'Sir, please don't fight the lion. You'll die. Come away from here.'

'Sancho, leave me here. Go with Don Diego de Miranda. Perhaps I will die. Then tell Dulcinea about my adventures and about my love for her.'

The driver opened the box, and then he ran after the other men and horses. Don Quixote sent Rocinante with Sancho Panza. The horse was afraid of lions.

With his lance in his hand, Don Quixote walked slowly up to the open box. The lion saw the knight and opened his mouth very wide. Now everybody could see his long teeth.

'Come out of there,' shouted Don Quixote.

The lion looked at him with his dark yellow eyes. Then, slowly, the animal stood up. He turned round and sat down again. He closed his eyes. Was he asleep?

'Pull him out of that box,' Don Quixote shouted at the driver.

'Never!' said the man. 'He'll kill me. Be happy with your day's work. We know that you won this fight. The lion was afraid of you, so he stayed in his box.'

'You're right,' said Don Quixote happily. 'Write this story down. Show it to the king. Tell him that Don Quixote de la Mancha is not afraid of dangerous lions.'

Sancho Panza and the other men ran back to Don Quixote. 'Look at this!' cried Sancho Panza. 'My knight isn't dead.'

'From this day,' Don Quixote told everybody, 'please call me the Knight of the Lions.'

Don Diego de Miranda invited Don Quixote and Sancho Panza to his big house. They stayed there and ate and drank with Don Diego's family and friends. After four nights at the rich man's house, Don Quixote said, 'Thank you for your good food and conversation. But I'm a knight. I want to be on the road and to do good. Squire Sancho and I are going to have some more adventures.'

'Don Quixote, my family and I enjoyed your exciting stories. Visit us again one day and tell us more about your life,' said Don Diego.

When Don Quixote and Sancho Panza began their journey again, they stopped one night at an inn. They sat at a table and waited for their dinner. Suddenly, a big, loud man came through the door.

'Innkeeper! Have you got any rooms for tonight?' the man shouted.

'Pedro!' cried the innkeeper. 'This will be a good evening. Your theatre company is the best in the country. We always have rooms for you and your men.'

'Thank you, sir. I'll be back in a minute.' Pedro called his men. Then he went into the kitchen and asked some questions about the people in the inn that night.

When Pedro was in the other room, Don Quixote asked, 'Who is this man? Is he famous?'

'Yes, he's famous in every town round here. He has a theatre company, and he has a very clever **monkey**. The animal can look at you and see inside your head. Then he tells Pedro everything about you. He isn't always right, but usually he is.'

monkey /ˈmʌŋki/ (n) *Monkeys* are animals from hot countries. They are good climbers and usually live in trees.

36

When Pedro came back with his men and his monkey, Don Quixote asked the animal a question about his future.

'Sir,' said Pedro, 'the animal can't tell you about the future. He only knows about your old life.'

'That's no good to us,' said Sancho Panza. 'We know our old stories. Tell me about my wife, Teresa Panza. What's she doing at home at this minute? That's interesting to me.'

Pedro called to his monkey. The animal talked quickly into the man's ear for a minute. Then it jumped down. Pedro suddenly turned to Don Quixote and took his hat from his head.

'You're the great Don Quixote de la Mancha. You're on an important journey. You're making the world a better place for everybody. You understand the life of a good knight.'

'How do you know this about me?' asked Don Quixote. 'This is my first visit to this place.'

But Pedro was cleverer than his monkey. He always asked questions about people before he talked to them. He knew a lot of stories about Don Quixote and Sancho Panza from his conversation in the kitchen.

'And you, Sancho, are the best squire in the world and the best friend to your knight. Don't be unhappy about your wife. She's working, and she's got a bottle of wine near her hand.'

'You know my wife,' said Sancho Panza. But he felt afraid of this man and his monkey.

Don Quixote and Sancho Panza stayed away from Pedro and the monkey that night, and they left the inn early in the morning.

5.1 Were you right?

Look back at your answers to Activity 4.4. Then finish these sentences.

Sancho Panza finds a man with twenty ᵃ .... and buys some ᵇ .... from him. He carries it in the doctor's ᶜ .... But Don Quixote wants his helmet and quickly puts it on his head. The milk runs through Don Quixote's ᵈ .... and down his face.

Don Quixote wants to fight with the ᵉ .... in the large ᶠ .... The animal is hungry and dangerous and has long ᵍ .... Sancho and the ʰ .... men watch. Don Quixote wins the 'fight'.

Pedro and his ⁱ .... little animal arrive at the inn. They are with a ʲ .... company. The ᵏ .... speaks into Pedro's ear. Sancho is afraid of it.

5.2 What more did you learn?

Match the men and animal on the right with the words in *italics*.

1 '*He*'s always playing games with me.'
2 '*He*'s getting very hungry, so *he*'s very dangerous.'
3 '*He*'s always looking for a good adventure.'
4 'Tell *him* that Don Quixote is not afraid of dangerous lions.'
5 *He* enjoys Don Quixote's stories.
6 *He* always asks questions about people before he talks to them.
7 *He* feels afraid of Pedro and the monkey.

Don Quixote
the king
Pedro
Sancho Panza
Frestón
Don Diego
the lion

.3 Language in use

Read the sentences in the box.
Then finish the words in *italics*
with *s* or *'s*.

'He**'s** always playing game**s** with me.'

After four night**s** at the rich man**'s** house, Don Quixote wanted to leave.

1 Don Quixote usually forgot about his *problem*..... .'I understand *Frestón*.... *game*..... . *He*.... not as clever as I am.'

2 '*What*.... this? *There*.... something in my *eye*.... .'

3 *There*.... an animal in the box. Don *Quixote*.... new friend, Don Diego, *think*.... that *it*.... the *king*.... lion.

4 Does the monkey really know about Don *Quixote*.... life and about *Sancho*.... wife? Or does Pedro know *thing*.... from his *conversation*.... in the *innkeeper*.... kitchen?

.4 What happens next?

How are Sancho Panza's old life and his new life different? Write notes in this table.

	Old life	New life
1 Food	good food and wine	
2 Bed	slept in his house	
3 Work	difficult; little money	
4 People	wife and children	
5 Adventures	no	

CHAPTER 5

Good King Sancho

'I have a small country!' shouted Don Carlos excitedly. 'The old king died this year. Sancho Panza can be the king of Baratario.'

Don Quixote and Sancho Panza left the inn and forgot about the monkey and the theatre company. They were happier on the road. But Sancho began to think about his home and family.

'Sir, I felt strange when I met that monkey. How did it know about my wife? Perhaps I'll go home and look after my family. Is it better to be your squire or a husband and father? Also, at home I have food and wine every day, and I have a bed a night. With you, I have two metres of hard ground at night and nothing in my stomach.'

'It's your life, Squire Sancho,' said Don Quixote. 'Take the road to your house or follow me. I'll pay you for your work. How much will it be?'

'I worked for the father of Sansón Carrasco, sir, when I was young. He paid me two **ducats*** each month. He also gave me a good dinner at night and a nice bed. I never have these things from you.'

'What do you think, Sancho? How much for your work and for food? And don't forget the bed!'

'I think three ducats for my work. And two ducats more because I'm not going to be a king now.'

'A king? Where does that idea come from? Did I say that, Squire Sancho?'

'I remember your words very well,' said Sancho Panza. 'I was twenty years younger, and you were too.'

Don Quixote started to laugh, but it was a cold laugh. 'Twenty years! No, Sancho, that's not possible – two months, perhaps. But take my money, and go home. I hope that you're happier there. But you'll never be a king. I won't find a small country for you. You're a donkey, not a king. You'll be a donkey today, tomorrow and after you die.'

---

* **Ducats** were money in some European countries.

Sancho Panza felt sorry and began to cry. 'Sir,' he said, 'you're right! I really am a donkey. Don't listen to me. I haven't got a lot of ideas in my head. Sometimes I talk too much. Please, I don't want to stop being your squire. I'd like twenty more years with you.'

'OK,' Don Quixote said. 'I'll give you your job back this time. And I'll find a country for you too. We'll have another twenty years and a lot of new adventures!'

That night, the knight and his squire slept under another tree. In the morning they saw some people on fine horses on the road.

'Look at these rich people, sir,' said Sancho Panza.

'Sancho, do you see the beautiful woman on the white horse? Run to her. Say that Don Quixote de la Mancha, the Knight of the Lions, wants to meet her. Speak nicely to her.'

Sancho ran to the woman. 'Madam, my knight, Don Quixote de la Mancha, is near here. He wants to speak to you. He'll help you in some way. People call him the Knight of the Lions.'

'Wait! I have a book about this knight,' said the lovely rich woman. 'Does he love a girl with the name Dulcinea del Toboso?'

'That's right! And I'm Don Quixote's squire. My name is . . .'

'You're Sancho Panza. Am I right?'

'Yes, madam. I am.' Sancho Panza felt very happy. A beautiful, important woman knew his name.

'My name is Doña Maria,' the woman said. 'I want to invite you and your knight to my castle. It's very near here. Please tell your knight.'

Sancho Panza found Don Quixote and told him about the woman on the white horse. The two men then went quickly back to Doña Maria.

The woman was very excited. She thought, 'My husband and I read about this strange man and his adventures in a book by Cide Hamete Benengeli. We're going to enjoy our time with him and his squire. We'll play some funny games with them. People don't usually follow ideas from old books. But Don Quixote is really living the life of a knight. This is very interesting!'

'Let's go to my castle,' Doña Maria said to Don Quixote and Sancho Panza. 'You'll meet my husband, Don Carlos, there.'

That evening after dinner, Don Quixote talked to Don Carlos and his beautiful wife.

'I'm going to find a small country for Sancho Panza one day,' said Don Quixote. 'He'll be the king of the place.'

'I have a small country!' shouted Don Carlos excitedly. 'The old king died this year. Sancho Panza can be the king of Baratario.'

'I would like to try,' said Sancho Panza. 'A good squire will be a good king, I think. Can I take my donkey with me? I know that many donkeys work for kings. And many kings are donkeys.'

Doña Maria laughed at these words. She liked Sancho Panza very much and enjoyed his conversation. 'Now, Squire Sancho, go to bed and sleep well. You'll have a lot of work tomorrow.'

When everybody in the house was asleep, Don Carlos and Doña Maria talked and laughed about their strange visitors. 'We'll have to tell the five thousand people in the town of Baratario about King Sancho so they're ready for him, their first king,' said Don Carlos. 'When he arrives, the people can't laugh at him. They have to meet their king and take him to the castle. We can't tell Sancho Panza about our game. Later, we'll enjoy many stories about the town's fat little king.'

At the same time, Don Quixote had an interesting conversation with Sancho. 'This is wonderful. Tomorrow you'll be the King of Baratario.'

'Thank you for this, sir. Do you think that I'll be a good king?'

'Yes! But remember your old life – when you weren't a rich or an important man. And don't forget your friends and family. Help people when you can. Cut your hair and wash every day. Wear clean clothes and good shoes. Don't ask for a lot of money. Walk slowly. Speak quietly. Drink very little wine.'

'Thank you, Don Quixote,' said Sancho Panza. 'But I can't remember all of that. Can you write your words on paper for me? I know I can't read. But a king has helpers. They can read these words to me every day.'

'But a king has to read and write,' said Don Quixote. 'Can you write your name?'

'Yes, I learned that from Sansón Carrasco's father. But do you think I'm going to be good at this job? I don't have to be a king. I can be the old Sancho and be happy.'

'These are intelligent words. My plan worked. You're ready now for the people of Baratario. You'll be a king and I'll be your knight.'

The next day, Sancho Panza dressed in fine clothes and went to his new country. The important men of the town of Baratario met their new king at the church. Then they took him to his castle. King Sancho sat down and waited. He wanted to begin his job.

'King Sancho, you are the king of a very important country, so you have many important jobs,' said one of his new helpers.'

'Yes, I understand,' said Sancho Panza. 'And I want to be a good king. What is my first job?'

'There are many problems in Baratario. You will have to find answers to every problem, big and small,' said the helper.

'I'll be very busy,' said Sancho. 'Will I have time for food or sleep?'

'No, not really. The king has to help his people night and day. Look, here is your first problem.'

Two old men came into the room. One of the men used a **walking stick** because his legs weren't very strong.

walking stick /ˈwɔːkɪŋ stɪk/ (n) You use a *walking stick* when you cannot walk well.

'Please tell me about your problem,' said Sancho Panza to the old man without a walking stick.

'Sir, last year my friend asked me for some money, but only for a month or two. I gave him two ducats. But after more than a year, I'm waiting for my money. Now my friend says that he gave me the money in April. Perhaps he gave me my money, but I can't remember.'

'How can I help?' asked Sancho Panza.

'Ask him about the money. You're the king. He'll tell *you*.'

'What do you say about this, old man with the walking stick?' Sancho Panza asked the second man.

'Sir, I gave the money back to him in April,' said the second man.

'Will you put your hands on the Bible and repeat those words?' asked Sancho Panza.

'Yes, I will,' said the second old man. Then he turned to his friend. 'Please take my walking stick for a minute.'

Then he put his two hands on the Bible. 'I haven't got my friend's two ducats. I gave this money back to him.'

'Are you happy now?' King Sancho asked the first old man.

'Yes, perhaps he *did* give me my money, and I forgot about it.'

Then the second old man took his walking stick again and the two friends left the room.

Sancho Panza sat in his king's chair and thought about the two ducats. Suddenly he shouted, 'Bring those two old men back to me.' When they were in front of Sancho Panza, he looked at them carefully. 'Give me your walking stick,' he said to the second old man.

'Here it is, sir,' said the man.

King Sancho broke the stick and two ducats fell on the floor.

Sancho turned and spoke to the first old man. 'When you came here, your friend gave the walking stick to you and *then* he put his hands on the Bible. When he finished talking, he took the walking stick – and your money – back. But I understood his game. Now you've got your money again. Take it and go home.'

Sancho Panza worked very hard and helped the people of Baratario in many other ways. He put better and cheaper food and wine in the shops. Clothes and shoes were cheaper too. He helped the people with problems with the banks and paid them the right number of ducats for their work. Under King Sancho, families could walk happily at night in the clean, friendly streets and parks. He was, the people of Baratario thought, an intelligent and good king.

But Sancho Panza wasn't very happy in Baratario because he never got a good breakfast, lunch or dinner. Three times a day, he sat down at his table. The cook put food on his plate, but then the king's doctor looked at the food. 'Wait, sir! This isn't food for a king. Take it away!' he shouted.

In the end, Sancho Panza was very angry. 'Doctor, leave this castle and don't come back,' he shouted. 'I want to eat!'

But then a letter came from Don Carlos. It said: 'King Sancho, be careful. There are bad men in Baratario. They want to kill you. Don't eat the food from your table.'

This was another of Don Carlos's games. He and Doña Maria enjoyed hearing the stories about Baratario's king.

Sancho Panza felt afraid, but he was also angry. 'I can't live without food,' he shouted. He had some bread and water for dinner. He was very hungry when he went to bed.

In the night, Sancho Panza heard a lot of loud noise. 'Wake up, King Sancho,' his helpers shouted. 'There are men outside the town walls. They want to take Baratario from us. Please help your people!'

'I'm not a fighter. Call for Don Quixote. He loves a good fight.'

'No, you're our king. Put on your suit of armour and stop these men.'

They brought Sancho Panza a suit of armour. It was very small, and he couldn't move in it. Then the lights went out, and he fell to the floor. He couldn't see anything or anybody. There was a lot of noise and smoke. Men ran in and out of the king's bedroom. Some men jumped over the king. Some kicked him. Everybody shouted.

Then suddenly the noise stopped, and the game ended. The king's men cried, 'We won! Baratario is ours! Stand up, King Sancho. You're now Sancho the Great!'

But Sancho Panza didn't want to be a king. In the morning, he spoke to the people of Baratario. 'I came here without a penny, and I'm leaving without a penny. I think that is a good thing in a king. But I wasn't born for this life. I'm going to go back on the road with my knight, Don Quixote de la Mancha. Goodbye.'

6.1 Were you right?

Look at your answers to Activity 5.4. Then write A and B in the right places.

	At home	With Don Quixote
1 **A** a squire **B** a husband and father		
2 **A** food and wine every day **B** nothing in his stomach		
3 **A** two metres of hard ground **B** a bed		
4 **A** a villager **B** a king		

6.2 What more did you learn?

How does Sancho Panza feel at these times: happy (✓) or unhappy (✗)? Discuss why.

1 At the inn with Pedro and the monkey

2 When he meets Doña Maria

3 At dinner in Don Carlos's house

4 After Don Quixote talks to him about a king's job

5 When the king's doctor looks at his food

6 When he gets a letter from Don Carlos

7 When he has to wear a suit of armour

8 On the road again with Don Quixote

5.3 Language in use

**Read the sentence in the box.
Then use past tense verbs in these
sentences from the story.**

> Don Quixote and Sancho Panza
> **left** the inn and **forgot** about the
> monkey and the theatre company.

'He ....
me two ducats each
month.'

Sancho Panza
....
to cry.

Sancho Panza
....
to the woman.

The second old man
.... his
walking stick again.

King Sancho
....
the stick.

Sancho Panza
....
a lot of loud noise.

6.4 What happens next?

**Read the name of Chapter 6 and the sentence in *italics* below it. Then
look at the pictures in this chapter. Write a sentence about each picture.**

1 ....

2 ....

3 ....

4 ....

CHAPTER 6

The Last Days of Don Quixote

*'My books about knights were wrong, and I was stupid. I, Alonso Quixada
– not Don Quixote – am going to die, and I am ready.'*

Before Don Quixote and Sancho Panza left Don Carlos's castle, Don
Carlos gave Sancho a bag of money for his work in Baratario. The
knight and his squire liked Don Carlos and Doña Maria very much, but
they were happier on the road. That same day, they met some young
people and had an adventure.

'Hello!' shouted one of the young men. 'Come and have some food
and wine with us.'

Don Quixote was interested in these young people. 'What are you
doing here in the middle of these trees?' he asked. 'Where are your
homes?'

'We live near here. But we want to learn about people from a different
time. We want to have good, happy lives.'

'Young friends, I have the same idea. My name is Don Quixote de la
Mancha.'

'We know everything about you,' said one of the young women
excitedly. 'We read a book about you last year. You're the best knight in
the world. You're famous for your adventures and your good work. And
your friend has to be Sancho Panza.'

'You're right about that,' said Sancho happily. 'I'm the famous squire from your famous book!'

'And we know about Dulcinea del Toboso. Isn't she the most beautiful woman in Spain?' asked one of the boys.

'She's the most beautiful woman in the world!' said Don Quixote. 'My journeys and fights are all for her.'

The two older men ate and drank and talked about their adventures with the young men and women. They enjoyed a very nice afternoon.

'How can I thank you for this very fine lunch and good conversation?' asked Don Quixote at the end of the day. 'I'll stand in the middle of the road for two days and nights. I'll tell everybody about these fine young women. They aren't as wonderful as my love, Dulcinea, but I'll sing about them to the world.'

The young people watched Don Quixote. After an hour or two, a hundred **bull**s came down the road. A number of men on horses followed behind them. The animals ran very fast, and the boys and girls ran quickly behind some trees. But Don Quixote didn't move. He sat on his horse with his lance in his hand.

'Move, sir,' shouted one of the men. 'These animals will kill you. Get out of the way!'

'Bulls! They're nothing to Don Quixote de la Mancha.'

The hundred bulls ran over Don Quixote and Rocinante and went down the road very quickly with the men behind them.

---

bull /bʊl/ (n) *Bulls* are large, strong animals. People say that the colour red makes *bulls* angry.

After a minute or two, Don Quixote stood up and shouted after the bulls. 'Are you afraid of one knight? Come back and fight me!' But the adventure was at an end. Don Quixote climbed slowly on to Rocinante.

Sancho Panza ran to him. 'Your horse is fine, but are you hurt, sir?'

'Let's not talk about that, Squire Sancho.' And with sad smiles, Don Quixote and Sancho Panza left that place and those friendly young people.

That evening, the two men stopped at the door of an inn near the city of Saragossa. Sancho Panza spoke to the innkeeper about some dinner. At the same time, Don Quixote was in his room. He could hear a conversation in the room next to his.

'Don Jerónimo, before dinner let's read some pages from that new book, *Don Quixote de la Mancha*,' said a man.

'Don Juan, why do you want to read that book? It's really not very interesting,' said Don Jerónimo.

'But,' said Don Juan, 'I want to know more about Dulcinea del Toboso. Why did Don Quixote's love for her die?'

When Don Quixote heard these words, he jumped out of his chair.

'Don Quixote will never forget Dulcinea del Toboso. He'll always love her and fight for her!' the knight shouted.

The three men came out of their rooms at the same time.

'Are you really Don Quixote?' asked Don Jerónimo. 'Do you know the stories in this book?' He gave the book to Don Quixote.

'Don't read these stories,' said Don Quixote. 'This writer doesn't know anything about me or my adventures. Read the book about me by Cide Hamete Benengeli. Forget about this new book.'

'Sir, we would like to hear everything from *you*. Please eat and drink with us this evening,' said Don Jerónimo.

'Thank you. But first, remember one thing. I love Dulcinea del Toboso. She's the most beautiful, the most wonderful woman in the world.' And then the three men had dinner and talked for many hours.

Before Don Quixote went to bed, Don Juan asked him about his plans. 'Are you going to Saragossa tomorrow, Don Quixote? You usually go there for the big fights at this time of year.'

'Why do you say that?' asked Don Quixote.

'We read about your adventures in Saragossa in our book.'

'But your book is not about me. I didn't go to Saragossa last year, and I will not go there tomorrow or next year.'

'I understand,' said Don Jerónimo. 'There are big fights in Barcelona too. Perhaps you are going there.'

Don Quixote liked this idea. 'That's my plan,' he said. 'Good night.'

Don Juan and Don Jerónimo threw their book into the fire. They knew Don Quixote now, and he wasn't the knight in that book.

Some days later, Don Quixote and Sancho Panza arrived in Barcelona. This was the first visit to the sea for the knight and his squire. Sancho Panza looked at the sea and at the big ships with their sails. 'What are these?' he asked. 'Are they windmills or large animals? How many feet have they got?'

One fine morning, Don Quixote got on Rocinante and went to the beach in his suit of armour. Suddenly he saw another knight, also on a horse and in a suit of armour. When the knight was near Don Quixote, he shouted, 'Great Don Quixote de la Mancha, listen to me. I am the Knight of the White Mountains. I want to fight with you. The love of my life is more beautiful than Dulcinea del Toboso.' Don Quixote looked at him angrily. 'Ah! Do you want to fight me? Lose, and you have to go back home for a year. Win, and I'll give you my horse, my suit of armour and my money. Quick! What's your answer?'

'Sir, I don't know you,' Don Quixote answered, 'but perhaps you're a famous knight. You're making a mistake. Dulcinea is the most wonderful, the most beautiful woman in the world. I'll fight you and then you'll tell everybody about her. I'm ready. Are you?'

The two horses ran as fast as possible and the knights began their fight. But the Knight of the White Mountains and his horse were bigger, heavier and stronger than Don Quixote and Rocinante. They hit the smaller knight and his horse very hard and threw them to the ground. This time Don Quixote and Rocinante were badly hurt.

The Knight of the White Mountains jumped from his horse and put his lance on Don Quixote's stomach. 'Go home for a year or you're a dead man,' he shouted.

'But Dulcinea is the most beautiful woman in the world,' Don Quixote answered weakly. 'I will die for her. Kill me now!'

'No,' said the Knight of the White Mountains. 'You're a fine knight. I won't kill you, but go home.'

'You're kind, sir. I *will* go home,' said Don Quixote. 'But you won't say anything bad about Dulcinea.'

'Right!' said the Knight of the White Mountains. Then he quickly left Barcelona.

Some men from the city followed him and stopped him outside the city. 'Sir, what's your name?' they asked. 'Why did you come to Barcelona?'

'I'm Sansón Carrasco from Don Quixote's village in La Mancha. I'm one of his best friends. I lost a fight to him last year. His life of adventure is dangerous and stupid. Without his ideas on knights and adventures, he is a very intelligent man and a good friend.'

'But we like this knight. We read the books and enjoy his adventures. Don Quixote and Sancho Panza make us happy. Don't change him. His old life was boring – to him and to us.'

'You're wrong. He will be happier at home with his friends.'

At the beach, Don Quixote and Rocinante were very weak. The knight's face was white and he couldn't walk. Some men carried him to a hospital in the city, and he stayed there for more than a week.

'Think of your future, sir,' Sancho said to Don Quixote. 'You have many good stories. Let's forget about adventures and go home for a time.'

'Yes, you're right, Squire Sancho. It's only for a year. After that we'll begin another journey. Perhaps you'll be a king again.'

'Perhaps. I hope that we'll have more adventures,' said Sancho Panza kindly. Then the two men followed the long road to their village in La Mancha.

But Don Quixote wasn't happy. When he arrived at his home, he said, 'Put me to bed, please. I'm not very well.'

Sancho Panza and Don Quixote's friends Pero, Nicolás and Sansón Carrasco sat next to the knight's bed and watched him. The friends wanted to talk to him. But Don Quixote was tired and slept for many hours every day. On the sixth day, the doctor visited. 'Don Quixote is not getting better,' he said.

And then Don Quixote woke up. He looked at his friends and cried, 'I know that this is the end now. My books about knights were wrong, and I was stupid. I, Alonso Quixada – not Don Quixote – am going to die, and I am ready.'

Our knight fell back on his bed. Three days later, he died with a smile on his face. That was the end of a good man and a fine knight.

1 **A newspaper writer wants to write a story about Don Quixote. He or she is going to talk to the people in the pictures. Work with four other students.**

  a Discuss the writer's questions for these people.
  b Have these conversations.

| Student A | You are the writer. Ask your questions. |

| Students B–E | You are the people in the pictures. Answer the writer's questions. |

2 **Discuss these questions.**

  a Why does the writer get a different idea of Don Quixote from different people?
  b Who really knew Don Quixote?
  c Who was Don Quixote's best friend? Why?

An Internet company is selling Don Quixote's things. Write about them for the Internet shop. You want people to pay a lot of money for them. Why are they important? How much do they cost?

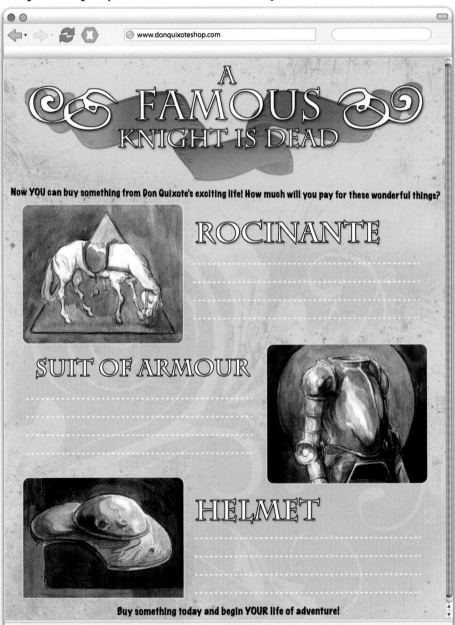

After high school and before university or a job, some young people try something different for a year. This is called a 'gap year'. Students on a gap year usually go to a different country. They want to find adventure, and they often want to change the world in a small way.

1 Read about two people's gap years. Discuss their adventures. Which of these gap years would you like to have? Why?

Patty Simpson

I live in London, so I'm a city girl. I went to Australia and learned about a different way of life. I got up at five o'clock in the morning and worked outside with animals all day. It was a hard job, but I loved it. I worked with five other young people. Sometimes in the evenings we cooked our food over an open fire and slept outside under a big mountain. It was the best year of my life.

Nick Lee

I'm from Toronto, Canada. I helped in a small school in Guatamala for children between five and twelve years old. These children have no mothers or fathers. I helped with the English classes. I also cooked and cleaned. The children were really great, and some of them write letters to me now. I also learned some Spanish. I want to go back to Guatemala after university.

2 Why do people take a gap year? What is most important, do you think? Number these from 1 (the most important) to 10 (very unimportant). Discuss your ideas with two or three other students.

- ◯ meet new people
- ◯ see a new country
- ◯ learn a new language
- ◯ help people with problems
- ◯ take a classes (in cooking, music ...)

- ◯ enjoy life with people my age
- ◯ get away from home
- ◯ forget about school for a year
- ◯ learn a new sport
- ◯ grow up

Where is a good place for a gap year? What do you think? Number places on the map with words from the box.

1 most beautiful   2 most exciting   3 most interesting
4 most dangerous   5 different   6 most expensive   7 cheapest
8 coldest   9 hottest   10 strangest

Have a conversation about plans for a gap year. Work in groups of three.

| Student A | You want to take a gap year before you begin university. Tell your parents about your plans. Where do you want to go? What do you want to do there? |

| Students B-C | You are Student A's parents. You don't like the idea of a gap year. You want your son or daughter to start university now. Ask about his or her plans and talk about the problems. |

5 Finish this page in the *Adventure Is Everything!* magazine.

Adventure Is Everything!

We are the company for you!
We help with everything for a great gap year.

Remember: You can't take much with you, but these are important:

strong shoes
_____
_____
_____
_____

Remember: In some places, people have very little money and problems with jobs, houses and schools. Be a good visitor and think about their feelings:

Don't eat at fast-food restaurants.
_____
_____

Remember: Some places are dangerous. Be an intelligent adventurer and remember:

Don't show your money to people.
_____
_____